Mother May I?

For Dorian! Thank you!

MOTHER MAY I?

A Post-Floydian Folly

SARAH BOXER

10/16/19

International Psychoanalytic Books (IPBooks)
New York / *www.IPBooks.net*

ISBN 978-1-949093-17-9

IPBOOKS.net
International Psychoanalytic Books

To the one I call mom
and the one who calls me mum

PREFACE

My Little Objects and Their Relations

I have some advice for you as you read *Mother May I?* Treat these tales of Dr. Floyd, Bunnyman, Melanin Klein, Melittle Klein, Little Hans, and Squiggle Piggle as a dream. Go with the flow. And if you need help figuring out what this dream could mean, go to the footnotes. They will ground you; they will keep you sane, maybe.

My first book, *In the Floyd Archives*, was an extended riff on Freud's case histories. In the sequel, *Mother May I?*, I turn from Freud to Melanie Klein and D. W. Winnicott, the British psychoanalysts who followed in his wake and developed what is now known as object relations theory. (This also means that I have turned from the Father to the Mother in a number of ways.)

But despite this historical bent, *Mother May I?* is really make-believe: Freud was not a bird. Bunnies are not known for their Oedipus complexes. Real lambs do not pull kittens out of their pockets. And a real mother would never analyze her own children... Oh, wait just a second... in the case of Melanie Klein, that's exactly what she did!

Well, never mind that. For the most part, *Mother May I?* is a fantasy land. While real people who share the same psychoanalyst do not, generally speaking, know each other beyond the waiting room, the animals that Dr. Floyd and Melanin Klein see are inter-linked—and sometimes in very intimate ways. Thus, Lambskin serves as a blanket for Bunnyman, a mother to Melanin Klein, and the feminine part of Mr. Wolfman. And although Squiggle-Piggle is a whole pig to himself, to his peers he's nothing but a tail.

vii

This means that all these creatures, though real to themselves, may not be so much encountering the others as imagining them. And this, in ridiculously literal terms, happens to be the basis for the object relations theory that Klein and Winnicott helped to found: the people one deals with in real life are not the people they are to themselves but rather objects that play a specific role in one's mind. In short, each character is not only a subject but also an object for others. As Christopher Bollas writes in *Being a Character*, the idea that one person perceives another accurately is "largely illusory." Which means we are all "free to invent one another...free to misperceive." So let the games begin!

INTRODUCTION

After the Floyd

When Dr. Floyd, bird and psychoanalyst, flies the coop at the end of *In the Floyd Archives*, he leaves his patients—Bunnyman, Wolfman and Rat Ma'am—holding the bag. They are all alone in the wilderness clutching nothing but a gunny sack containing their fellow analysand, Lambskin, who has just barely escaped being fleeced by Dr. Floyd's friend the evil Dr. Fleece. They are relieved to be alive. But with Dr. Floyd gone, what will become of these poor devils, dragging their partially analyzed neuroses behind them? Will they wander endlessly in the post-Floydian landscape, half treated, half mad?

It doesn't take a genius to figure out that bunny, rat, wolf, and lamb are screwed. These animals aren't just ordinary neurotics wandering in a wasteland. They are like the band of angry brothers described in Freud's 1912 book *Totem and Taboo* after they have killed their tyrannical father. They are Freud's followers after Freud's death. They are Moses's flock, post Moses, looking for the promised land. They will have to build a new society, a post-Floydian society. But what will it be like? And who will lead them?

My poor little animals don't know what to do. They set up a totem pole in honor of their dear departed Dr. Floyd and start playing games—Tag, Mother May I?, etc. But before long they are all bickering about the rules and realize they desperately need an umpire, or a mother, or someone, anyone, to watch them play. Eventually they decide that Lambskin, the silent one, will fill this role. And so it is that these Floydian animals begin to build the foundations of a post-Floydian society. It is a government of games. There is a lot of playing, of course. But what else?

This post-Floydian society takes a serious swerve when the leader of the group, Lambskin, reaches into her pocket and pulls out a small black sheep — Melanin Klein, who turns out to share many features with Melanie Klein, one of the founders of object relations theory. She's bossy. She analyzes children by playing with them. She loves talking about ka-ka and widdlers. She believes that very young kids feel envy and rage, especially against their mummies' ta-tas. And she loves drawing this rage out in kids, including her own — one girl kitten, Melittle Klein (a.k.a. Melittle Little) who takes after Melanie Klein's bitter daughter, Melitta; one destructive boy bunny, Hans Klein (a.k.a. Little Hans); and one boy pig, Squiggle Piggle, whose tail makes squiggly drawings, just as D.W. Winnicott and his child patients did in the Squiggle Game.

But what does all this portend for Bunnyman, Rat Ma'am, Wolfman, and Lambskin? Will Melanin Klein have the answers they need? Will they reach the promised land of psychic health and happiness? Will they ever get over their abandonment? Will Dr. Floyd return? Will they kill him if he does? Answers (and more questions) ahead...

The Smoking Pipes

Freud once said, "Sometimes a cigar is just a cigar." But that is not Floyd's philosophy. In his world, a pipe is never just a pipe. In the following pages, a smoking pipe dropped into the cartoon frame signals a Freudian or post-Freudian parallel. You can ignore the smoking pipes or follow them to their sources in the notes, beginning on page 151.

FLOYD ESCAPES GRAVITY

2

13

TOTEM AND TABOO

16

18

20

21

24

THE GOVERNMENT
OF GAMES

31

34

A LITTLE NIGHTCAP

43

44

46

48

49

THE RETURN
OF THE REPRESSED

55

57

MELANIN KLEIN

61

63

65

THE DEPRESSIVE POSITION

69

71

72

73

A PAINFUL EXTRACTION

77

78

79

80

81

LITTLE HANS
LEAPS IN

93

THE SQUIGGLE GAME

THE GOOD TA-TA

113

MOSES AND MAMATHEISM

116

119

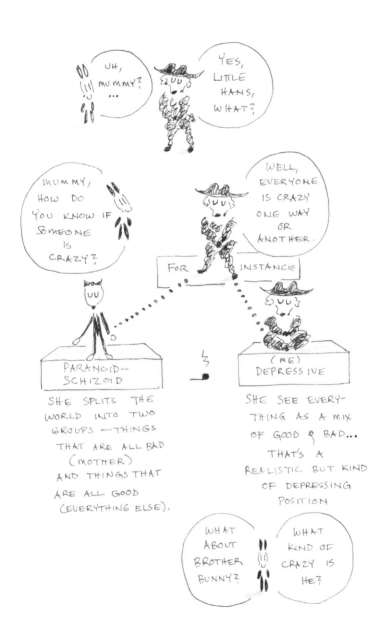

123

LIKE A GOD

126

128

129

ARMED AND DANGEROUS

136

140

THE PROMISED LAND

145

147

NOTES

The Smoking Pipes

p. 4: *We rescued you from Dr. Floyd's couch.* See *In the Floyd Archives: A Psycho-Bestiary*, by Sarah Boxer (Queens, New York: IP Books, 2019), pp. 124–125. At the end of the book Dr. Floyd, psychoanalyst and bird, abandoned his patients. Similarly, in the last decades of his life, Freud turned away from his individual cases (at least in his writing) and began focusing on grander topics—the foundations of civilization, the roots of religion, and the future of psychoanalysis—in such works as *The Question of Lay Analysis* (1926), *The Future of an Illusion* (1927), *Civilization and Its Discontents* (1930), *Analysis Terminable and Interminable* (1937), and *Moses and Monotheism* (1939).

p. 4: *And he was about to fleece you.* See *Freud: A Life for Our Time*, by Peter Gay (New York: W.W. Norton & Company, 1988), p. 84. Near the end of *In the Floyd Archives* (pp. 91–113), Dr. Floyd teamed up with his friend Dr. Fleece to try out a new kind of treatment for Lambskin's hysteria—hypnosis followed by a complete fleecing. We never catch sight of the evil quack Dr. Fleece, but he seems to share some key qualities with Freud's friend Wilhelm Fliess, an ear, nose, and throat doctor who had some crackpot ideas about surgical cures for psychological problems. Dr. Fliess recommended nose surgery to cure hysteria. Sadly, Freud took his advice in the case of Emma Eckstein, with some terribly gory results.

p. 5: *Dr. Floyd...he terminated us.* See *On Freud's 'Analysis Terminable & Interminable,'* edited by Joseph Sandler (New Haven: Yale University Press), pp. 4–6. Freud asked whether there really could be "such a thing as a natural end to an analysis." To illustrate the dangers of ending an analysis too soon, Freud cited the case of his own patient the Wolf Man, who had seemed cured of paranoia after only months of therapy but then, a decade later, was clearly back in the grip of it.

p. 8: *Are they plotting to kill me?* Freud outlined his violent vision of the origins of civilization in *Totem and Taboo: Resemblances Between the Mental Lives of Savages and Neurotics* (1913) and he recapped those ideas in *An Autobiographical Study* (1924) (New York: W. W. Norton & Company, 1989), pp. 75–80. Drawing on Darwin's vision of a primitive horde dominated by a single violent, powerful male, Freud imagined that the sons of a powerful father figure "one day...came together and united to overwhelm, kill, and devour their father, who had been their enemy but also their ideal."

p. 9: *Think effigy.* See "The Dynamics of the Transference" (1912), in *Collected Papers*, by Sigmund Freud (New York: Basic Books, 1959), Volume 2, translated under the supervision of Joan Riviere, p. 322. Freud wrote that "in the last resort, no one can be slain *in absentia* or *in effigie.*" This seemed to be his way of saying that the only way one can lay one's ghosts and psychic tormentors to rest is by first bringing them to life through transference, by transferring one's powerful feelings about these tormentors onto an analyst.

p. 10: *Whose woods are these?* Yes, it's roughly the beginning of a Robert Frost poem, but also part of the prehistory of the real Wolf Man, who lived on a huge Russian estate until he was five years old. See *The Wolf-Man by the Wolf-Man: The Double Story of Freud's Most Famous Case*, edited, with notes, an introduction, and four chapters, by Muriel Gardiner. (New York: Basic Books, 1971), pp. 4–5.

p. 11: *I think it will have wings.* See *Leonardo Da Vinci and a Memory of His Childhood* (1910), by Sigmund Freud (New York: W. W. Norton & Company, 1990), p. 32. Bunnyman shares some traits (particularly his impulse to sculpt and his obsession with birds) with Freud's vision of Leonardo da Vinci, who ascribed his own fascination with vultures to a childhood memory: "while I was in my cradle a vulture came down to me, and opened my mouth with its tail, and struck me many times with its tail against my lips."

p. 12: *Mr. Carnivore.* See "From the History of an Infantile Neurosis" (The Wolf Man, [1918]) in *Three Case Histories*, by Sigmund Freud, translated by Alix and James Strachey and edited by Philip Rieff (New York: Collier/Macmillan, 1963), p. 208–9. Freud's patient the Wolf Man was "cruel to small animals...in his imagination he liked beating large animals (horses) as well."

p. 13: *Bring us a bird...and the rest of us will share the guilt.* See *An Autobiographical Study* (1924), pp. 75–80. In his vision of how civilization might have begun, outlined in *Totem and Taboo*, Freud imagined that after the sons banded together and murdered their father or father figure (see note for p. 8), they would be full of remorse and would create the laws of totemism, "which aimed at preventing a repetition of such a deed." (They didn't want to be killed by their own sons, after all!) In this way the murdered father became a revered, totemic figure, more powerful in death than in life. Freud believed this "was the beginning at once of social organization, of religion, and of ethical restrictions."

p. 13: *His Biblical moment.* See Freud's paper "Obsessive Acts and Religious Practices" (1907) in *Collected Papers*, Volume 2, p. 26. Freud related religious rites, the very kind that Mr. Wolfman practices, to neurotic symptoms. "The neurotic ceremonial consists of little prescriptions, restrictions and arrangements in certain activities of everyday life which have to be carried out always in the same or in a methodically varied way."

p. 17: *Ooh, a totem pole!* See *An Autobiographical Study*, pp. 75–76. Animal phobias reflect a primitive fear of the father and therefore represent an "infantile recurrence of totemism." Also there is a "striking correspondence" between the twin rules of totemistic societies ("not to kill the totem and not to have sexual relations with any woman of the same totem-clan") and the twin wishes of the Oedipus complex (killing father and marrying mother).

p. 18: *The top, c'est moi!* On this totem pole, Dr. Floyd is the totem animal, which means he is this group's former prey as well as its current and future protector. It also means that Rat Ma'am, Bunnyman, Lambskin, and Wolfman are prohibited from eating all birds and all Floydians.

p. 25: *A tiny ritual wouldn't hurt!* See *An Autobiographical Study*, p. 77. In Freud's fantasy of the dawn of civilization, after the sons have killed the dominant male, they eat him and therefore internalize his power. Then, each year, to commemorate "the fearful deed" they sacrifice a totem animal, a stand-in for the murdered father. This is the "totem feast." In the Floydian world, it's a weenie roast.

p. 29: *Lambskin—our very own lay analyst.* See *The Question of Lay Analysis* (1926), by Sigmund Freud (Author), James Strachey (General Editor), with an introduction by Peter Gay (New York: W.W. Norton, 1990). A lay analyst is one who practices psychoanalysis without a medical degree. Freud argued that a medical degree was not necessary for psychoanalysts; indeed, he saw the medicalization of analysis as an American perversion. Technically, Lambskin is not so much a lay analyst as a layabout analyst.

p. 30: *We're not Floydians anymore.* D.W. Winnicott, one of the British psychoanalysts working in Freud's wake, is rumored to have said, while responding to a prospective psychoanalytic trainee who wanted "something different," something non-Freudian, "But we are all Freudian…more or less."

p. 30: *And rituals! Don't forget rituals!* See Freud's paper "Obsessive Acts and Religious Practices" (1907). Freud's Wolf Man was particularly fixated on religious-type rituals, which Freud related to obsessional behavior. Mr. Wolfman is also this way.

p. 31: *She could be like a mother…watching us play.* See *The Language of Winnicott: A Dictionary of Winnicott's Use of Words*, by Jan Abram (London: Karnac Books, 1996), pp. 316–334. Play therapy was one of the main inventions of the British Psycho-Analytic Society after Freud's death. Melanie Klein, the pioneer of object-relations therapy, used toys to bring out what she saw as the child's natural (and naturally conflicted) aggression. D.W. Winnicott, Klein's onetime follower, invented the Spatula Game, in which a shiny object is presented to the baby and the analyst sits back to see what happens. He also invented the Squiggle Game, in which the analyst and child would take turns drawing on the same piece of paper. (For more on the Squiggle Game, see note for p. 97.)

p. 36: *What do I want?... What do I want?* See *The Life and Work of Sigmund Freud,* Volume. 2, by Ernest Jones (New York: Basic Books, 1955), p. 421. "What does a woman want?" was the infamous question Freud formulated in a letter to Marie Bonaparte.

p. 37: *I always thought the goal of Mother May I was... to get closer to mother.* See "Analysis of a Phobia in a Five-Year-Old Boy" (Little Hans [1901]) in *Collected Papers,* by Sigmund Freud, edited by Ernest Jones (New York: Basic Books, 1959), Volume 3, translated by Alix and James Strachey, p. 253. The most important pleasure of Freud's "Little Hans" was "sleeping beside his mother." Likewise, Bunnyman is a perfect little Oedipus who will do just about anything to snuggle up to his mother.

p. 38: *And this mother is too depressed to handle it.* See *Winnicott,* by Adam Phillips (Cambridge: Harvard University Press, 1988), p. 90. In the paper titled "Reparation in Respect of Mother's Organized Defense against Depression" (1970), Phillips notes, "Winnicott writes about the infant or child with a depressed mother." Apparently, Donald Winnicott himself was such a child. See *Winnicott: Life and Work,* by F. Robert Rodman (New York: Perseus, 2003), pp. 13–14, where the author notes that Winnicott's mother "was a depressed woman and that Donald took it as his task to provide her with relief... to bring her back to life."

p. 39: *It's just Tag.* In Australia, Belgium, Canada, Ireland, New Zealand, South Africa, the U.K., and the English-speaking Caribbean, a game similar to Tag is called "What's the Time, Mr. Wolf?"

p. 39: *Where 'It' was, there 'I' shall be!* See *Freud and Man's Soul: An Important Reevaluation of Freudian Theory,* by Bruno Bettelheim (New York: Vintage Books, 1983), p. 54. Freud's famous dictum, "*Wo Es war, soll Ich werden,*" from his *New Introductory Lectures on Psychoanalysis* (1932), is usually translated as "Where id is, there shall ego be." Bruno Bettelheim recommended a more literal translation, "Where it is, there shall I be."

p. 44: *Romulus and Remus times.* See *Art and Artist: Creative Urge and Personality Development,* by Otto Rank (New York: Tudor Publishing Company, 1932), p. 197. Freud's onetime follower Otto

Rank put Romulus and Remus in the same basket as Moses: Usually, "the heroic city-founder is a foundling who has been turned adrift and is...suckled by an animal foster-mother (like the Roman she-wolf)...He has lost the maternal protection at too tender an age and finds compensation in the city which he founds..." (Moses, left in the bushes, founded the Jewish state, and Romulus and Remus were the castaway twin founders of Rome.) Bunnyman might go in this same basket: he lost his mother at an early age. However, he hasn't yet founded a state or found a replacement mother. For some more examples of fictional heroes who lost their mothers as kids, see my essay, "Why Are All the Cartoon Mothers Dead," *The Atlantic*, July–August, 2014.

p. 45: *Ow! Smack!* In *Leonardo da Vinci and a Memory of His Childhood*, Freud interpreted Leonardo Da Vinci's painting *The Virgin and Child with St. Anne* as an allusion to Leonardo's infant memory of a vulture coming down to him in the cradle, opening his mouth, and striking his lips with its tail. (See note for p. 11.) Freud interpreted the vulture story as a homosexual fantasy based on Leonardo's memory of nursing. In support of this idea, Freud noted that Egyptian hieroglyphs often represent the mother as a vulture.

p. 46: *Caw, caw, caw, saw, saw, saw.* Bunnyman, my little Oedipus, is worried about who saw him trying to have a nightcap of mother's milk. In the Oedipus myth, blindness and sight are recurring motifs. Oedipus is famous for his insights, but is blind about his own situation (that he killed his father, Laius, and then married his mother, Jocasta). When his eyes are opened to the truth, he blinds himself. A similar inverse relationship between insight and sight holds for the blind prophet Tiresias, who appears in the Oedipus story.

p. 48: *It seemed like a dream.* See note for pp. 45–46.

p. 49: *Here I am, Dr. Floyd!* When Moses meets God in the wilderness, God calls out to him from a burning bush and Moses answers: *Hineni!* (Here I am!)

p. 55: *Does my nose look fat?* See *The Wolf-Man by The Wolf-Man*, p. 272. Although Freud originally believed the Wolf Man case (1909) proved the efficacy of psychoanalysis, by the mid 1920s he knew the Wolf Man's analysis was far from complete. The Wolf Man's neurosis returned in the form of nose and tooth pain (and some murderous thoughts about Freud). Ruth Mack Brunswick, Freud's friend and student, took over the case. She wrote: "It was on Easter Day, 1925, that the nose symptoms reappeared. While the patient was sitting with his wife in a park he became aware of a painful sensation in his nose. He borrowed his wife's pocket-mirror..." to see what it was.

p. 56: *Repressed material.* See *The Language of Psycho-Analysis*, by J. Laplanche and J.-B. Pontalis, translated by Donald Nicholson-Smith (New York: W.W. Norton & Company, 1973), p. 398. Freud noted that repressed material has a "tendency to reenter into consciousness...by more or less devious routes," as slips, fantasies, and dreams. Freud termed this "the return of the repressed."

p. 57: *Dr. Floyd's glasses have fallen into my hands.* See *The Collected Papers*, Volume 3, pp. 303–311. Here Dr. Floyd comes flying back to Rat Ma'am in the form of Dr. Floyd's glasses. This event recalls Freud's case of the Rat Man, whose great obsessive fear centered on whether or not he had repaid a certain lieutenant for a pair of eyeglasses that were bought for him. It is also a concrete instance of "the return of the repressed."

p. 57: *Wolfman thinks that Dr. Floyd is punishing him.* See Ruth Mack Brunswick's supplement to Freud's Wolf Man case history in *The Wolf-Man by The Wolf-Man*, p. 284–285. As Brunswick notes, long after Freud's analysis of the Wolf Man had ended, the Wolf Man continued to have fantasies about Freud intervening in his analysis. The Wolf Man always wished "to be back in analysis with Freud" and believed that Freud kept checking up on him, which was not the case.

p. 60: *She has pockets?* See *Dora: An Analysis of a Case of Hysteria*, translated by Philip Rieff (New York: Collier/Macmillan, 1963), pp. 94–95. Freud writes that during her analysis, when Dora kept opening and shutting "her jewel case" (or *Schmuck-kästchen*, which happens to be a slang German term for female genitals) and poking her finger into it, this was her "entirely unembarrassed yet unmistakable pantomimic announcement of what she would like to do with them—namely to masturbate." (See also *In the Floyd Archives*, p. 55)

p. 61: *Melanin Klein.* See *Melanie Klein: Her World and Her Work*, by Phyllis Grosskurth (Cambridge, Mass.: Harvard University Press, 1986), p. 136. This little black sheep, whose name, Melanin Klein, literally means "Little Black," has an uncanny resemblance to Melanie Klein, who was famous for (among many things) her outlandish hats. Alix Strachey, a member of the Bloomsbury group, described one hat worn by *"Die Klein"* as follows: "It's a vasty, voluminous affair in bright yellow with a huge brim and a cluster, a whole garden, of mixed flowers somewhere up the back, side or front—The total effect is that of an overblown tea-rose with a slightly roug'd core...and the psychs will shudder. She looks like a whore run mad—or no—she really is Cleopatra..."

p. 62: *Are you a kid?* See *On the Psychoanalysis of Children* (1932), by Melanie Klein, with an authorized translation by Alix Strachey (New York: Delacorte Press, 1973), p. 16. Klein described the setup in her office: "On a low table in my analytic room there are laid out a number of small and simple toys: little wooden men and women, carts, carriages, motor-cars, trains, animals, bricks and houses, as well as paper, scissors and pencils. Even a child that is usually inhibited in its play will at least glance at the toys or touch them, and will soon give me a first glimpse into its complexes by the way in which it begins to play with them or lays them aside, or by its general attitude towards them."

p. 64: *Ah-ha! You banged my trains.* See *On the Psychoanalysis of Children*, pp. 16–18. Klein described the start of her analysis of a young boy, three years and nine months old: "At the very beginning of his first session Peter [who was, it turns out, Klein's older son, Hans] took the toy carriages and cars and put them first one behind the other and then side by side...He took two horse-drawn carriages and bumped one into another, so that the horses' feet knocked together, and said: 'I've got a new little brother called Fritz' [who was, it turns out, Klein's younger son, Erich]. I asked him what the carriages were doing. He answered: 'That's not nice,' and stopped bumping them together at once, but started again quite soon...."

In his second session...he once again...knocked two carriages together, and then two engines. He next put two swings side by side and, showing me the inner and longish part that hung down and swung, said: 'Look how it dangles and bumps.'" Klein explained to her son that he was actually representing his parents having sex as well as "his identification with both parents in coitus." Klein's analysis with her older son "Peter" occupied 278 sessions.

p. 64: *What's your word for pee-pee?* In a footnote in *The Psycho-Analysis of Children*, p. 17, Klein wrote, "I always find out beforehand from the child's mother what special words the child uses for the genitals, excremental processes, etc., and adopt them in speaking to it."

p. 65: *You have kids?* See *Melanie Klein: Her World and Her Work*, pp. 95–96. Klein was famous for psychoanalyzing children and infamous for psychoanalyzing her own children. Melitta, Klein's eldest child and only daughter, born in 1904, was written up as "Lisa," a 17-year-old girl, in Klein's paper "The Development of a Child"; she changed her name to Melitta Schmideberg when she married. Klein's second child, Hans, born in 1907, is "Peter" in the crashing-thingummies case (see first note for p. 64); he died a young man in a climbing accident in 1934. Klein's youngest child, Erich, born in 1914, appears as Peter's brother "Fritz" in some case histories; he was later was analyzed by D.W. Winnicott and changed his name to Eric Clyne.

p. 68: *Why yes, I, Melanin Klein, do have kids.* See *Melanie Klein*, by Julia Segal (London: Sage Publications Ltd., 2004), p. 66. Klein often referred to herself in the third person as Mrs. Klein.

p. 68: *Here she is—Melittle Klein!* See *Melanie Klein: Her World and Her Work*, p. 214, p. 461. Melittle Klein shares many features with Klein's only daughter, Melitta. Although Melitta did follow her mother in becoming a psychoanalyst, she (and her own analyst, Edward Glover) often attacked Klein and her obsession with mothers and their breasts. On one occasion, at a meeting of the British Psycho-Analytical Society, Melitta shouted at her mother: "Where is the father in your work?" then "stamped her foot and stormed out of the meeting." She never reconciled with her mother.

On Sept. 22, 1960, the day Melanie Klein died, Melitta "gave a lecture in London...wearing flamboyant red boots."

p. 69: *She wants to eat me alive...She never wants to stop sucking on me.* See *Melanie Klein*, by Julia Segal, p. 108. In contrast to Freud, who believed that children only feel guilt after the Oedipal phase, starting around age 6, Klein believed that guilt starts at infancy: "The earliest feelings of guilt in both sexes derive from the oral-sadistic desires to devour the mother, and primarily her breasts.... It is therefore in infancy that feelings of guilt arise."

p. 69: *I call it the depressive position...and it's as good as it gets.* See *Introduction to the Work of Melanie Klein*, by Hanna Segal (London: Karnac Books, 1973). In a significant departure from Freud, Klein viewed psychological states as "positions" (constellations of feelings, fantasies, and defenses) that can become active at any time in life, rather than as distinct stages of life. In the essays "A Contribution to the Psychogenesis of Manic Depressive States" (1934) and "Mourning in Relation to Manic Depressive States" (1940), Klein outlined the features of these two positions. In the more primitive state, "the paranoid-schizoid position," the person, who is unaware of, or unable to take in, whole persons, splits them into good and bad parts (thus the term "schizoid") and becomes paranoid about being attacked by the bad parts (thus "paranoid"). By contrast, "the depressive position," a more mature psychological state, is marked by the recognition of whole persons. The depressive position goes hand in hand with feelings of anxiety, guilt, ambivalence, and, as the name suggests, depression.

p. 71: *Popo-kaki.* See *The Selected Melanie Klein*, edited by Juliet Mitchell (New York: The Free Press, 1987), p. 61. Klein's four year old patient "Trude" used the word "*po-kacki-kucki*" for excrement. Here is a snippet of Klein's play-work with Trude: "She tried to tie my hands and feet, she lifted the sofa-cover and said she was making '*po-kacki-kucki*'." Klein interpreted this as the child "looking into the mother's 'popo' [her anus] for the kackis [feces], which to her represented children."

Klein wasn't the only analyst who witnessed children making the equation between ka-ka and babies. Winnicott noted such an equation in *The Piggle: An Account of the Psychoanalytic Treatment of a Little Girl* (Madison, Conn.: International Universities Press, 1977), p. 43: "I be a baby," the Piggle told him. "I want to be bryyyyyh.'" And "bryyyyyh," Winnicott noted, "meant feces." Long before Klein or Winnicott, Freud made the same parallel in the Rat Man case (see "Notes Upon a Case of Obsessional Neurosis" [1909] in *Collected Papers*, by Sigmund Freud, Volume 3, pp. 293–385) and in the case of Little Hans ("Analysis of a Phobia in a Five-Year-Old Boy," p. 217). There the boy notes a similarity between a "lumf" of ka-ka and a baby, noting "A lumf's much bigger."

    p. 72: *What has it got in its pocketses?* Rat Ma'am here echoes the Golem talking to Bilbo Baggins in *The Hobbit* by J.R.R. Tolkien.

    p. 73: *Popo-kaki…marbles…same difference.* See *Melanie Klein: Her World and her Work*, p. 129. In a letter to Alix Strachey dated December 24, 1924, Melanie Klein described a four-year-old patient: "She drew a glass jar in which there were marbles (small colored glass balls, etc.); on top of which she drew a lid, in order to close the glass jar so that the marbles would not fall out.…When, at this point, I gave my first interpretation that these were feces which she did not want her mother to produce…a changed relationship between us was established." This is not unlike a case of childhood constipation that Erik Erikson describes in *Childhood and Society* (1950).

    p. 76: *My dream was to be a doctor…"* See *Melanie Klein: Her World and Her Work*, p. 16. As a high-school student in Vienna, Melanie Klein dreamed of studying medicine and specializing in psychiatry. When she married at age 21, she abandoned the dream of a medical education.

    p. 76: *Help me, hurt me!* See *The Wolf-Man by The Wolf-Man*, pp. 272–276. A decade or so after the Wolf Man finished his analysis with Freud, his neurosis came roaring back in the form of nose and tooth pain, for which he sought physical relief. Ruth Mack Brunswick, the Wolf Man's psychoanalyst in the post-Freudian phrase, detailed each visit the Wolf Man made to various doctors and dentists. "On hearing from [one dentist] that the gum-boils were of no importance, he decided that he must have an additional opinion…"

And once his nose was fixed to his satisfaction, "his interest now returned to his teeth."

p. 77: *Lady Chatterley...Mrs. Batterby...Flying Chatterbee ...Mr. Bartleby...Madame Butterfly...* See *The Wolf-Man by the Wolf Man*, p. 231. Freud wrote that one day the Wolf Man, who was a rich young Russian, told him "that in his language a butterfly was called '*babushka*,' 'granny.' He added that in general butterflies had seemed to him like women and girls, and beetles and caterpillars like boys...Many months later, in quite another connection, the patient remarked that the opening and shutting of the butterfly's wings while it was settled on the flower had given him an uncanny feeling. It had looked, so he said, like a woman opening her legs, and the legs then made the shape of a Roman V, which, as we know, was the hour at which, in his boyhood, and even up to the time of the treatment, he used to fall into a depressed state of mind." Freud therefore interpreted the Wolf Man's butterfly phobia as related to his fear and repression of his feminine, anal desires.

p. 78: *Off to wash for surgery.* When the Rat Ma'am wears Dr. Floyd's glasses and becomes Mr. Wolfman's surgeon, she calls to mind Ruth Mack Brunswick, who was the Wolf Man's analyst after Freud. They even share initials and monosyllabic names: Ruth Mack, Rat Ma'am.

p. 78: *Eine Kleine Waschlappen.* The grandchild of a big bathmat—a.k.a. Lambskin—would be, of course, a tiny washcloth.

p. 78: *Always an object, never a subject.* See *Object Relations in Psychoanalytic Theory*, by Jay R. Greenberg and Stephen A. Mitchell (Cambridge: Harvard University Press, 1983), pp. 124–131. The branch of psychoanalysis Klein founded isn't called "object relations" for nothing. While Freud developed the idea of "internal parental voices," Klein developed the idea of "internal objects," the mental and emotional images of other people's bodies and body parts that populate each individual's internal world, starting at infancy. "Klein argues that [a child's] perceptions of real others [subjects] are merely a scaffolding for projections of the child's innate object images." Fittingly, the index to *Object Relations in Psychoanalytic Theory* cites 177 instances of the word "object" and not one of "subject."

p. 80: *Free treatment…for me?…from Dr. Floyd?* See *The Wolf Man's Magic Word: A Cryptonomy*, by Nicolas Abraham and Maria Torok, translated by Nicholas Rand, foreword by Jacques Derrida (Minneapolis: University of Minnesota Press, 1986), p. 8. After World War I, the Wolf Man, who had been a rich young man when Freud analyzed him, was poor and dependent. "The Russian ex-nabob, now an ordinary wage earner in Vienna, profited from the collective charity of analysts who enhanced his meager income; these sums were given to him every spring from 1919 on by Freud himself."

p. 80: *I've come for a painful exthraction.* See *The Wolf-Man by the Wolf-Man.* p. 273. In seeking treatment for his nose and tooth ailments, the Wolf Man seemed to favor painful treatments. Ruth Mack Brunswick described Dr. X's procedure to remove an infected gland on the Wolf Man's nose. "With the aid of an instrument he pressed the infected spot on the patient's nose; the patient cried out, and blood flowed from the place where the gland had been. As his analysis later revealed, he experienced at the sight of his own blood flowing under the doctor's hand an acute ecstasy. He drew a deep breath, hardly able to contain his joy."

p. 81: *Plink your sister? You have a sister?* See *The Wolf Man's Magic Word: A Cryptonomy*, p. 4–18. Abraham and Torok take a multilingual (Russian and German) approach to the Wolf Man's case, outlining the idea of cryptonyms—words, half-conscious, half-unconscious, that hide behind their foreign meanings. They suggest (p. 9), for instance, that we pay attention to "*the language of the nose*"—a wart that wanders from the Wolf Man's mother's nose to his sister's nose to his own nose, where he begs for it to be excised. As Abraham and Torok suggest, the way the "nose" problem moves from person to person expresses the Wolf Man's wish to tell the truth about his past sexual ties with both his sister and his father. They also suggest that the Wolf Man's nose symptoms, which were central to his analysis with Brunswick, expressed his guilt over the suicide of his sister, who had been depressed about her facial blemishes the night before she killed herself.

p. 81: *Here's a little sop to stop the bleeding.* See *The Interpretation of Dreams*, by Sigmund Freud, translated and edited by James

Strachey (New York: Avon Books, 1965), pp. 139–154. Mr. Wolfman's nose surgery is reminiscent of one of Freud's worst real-life nightmares, when his friend Wilhelm Fliess botched the nose surgery of Emma Eckstein by accidentally leaving a length of gauze in her nose. Freud recalled this terrible incident (and his dream of it) in his dream book.

p. 84: *It's me Little Hans. Or is it me Little Peter?* Melanie Klein, who was fascinated by Freud's Little Hans case, named her own son Hans Klein, which of course translates from her native tongue, German, to Little Hans. In her write-up of the case history of her son Hans Klein, she dubbed him Peter, which (at least in English) is slang for penis. See also note for p. 37.

p. 85: *Furious, envious, vengeful, murderous?* See *Envy and Gratitude and Other Works, 1946–1963*, by Melanie Klein (New York: The Free Press, 2002) and also *The Language of Winnicott*, pp. 87–88. In the essay "Envy and Gratitude," Klein describes envy and aggression toward the mother as part of every infant's emotional life. Winnicott, who was briefly Klein's follower, took issue with this idea, arguing that infants are too undifferentiated to feel envy or hatred. Indeed, he believed that there's really no such thing as an infant but rather only a mother-infant bond.

p. 86: *I've analyzed them both.* See notes for p. 64.

p. 87: *You mean you want to bump thingummies with me?* See notes for pp. 64–65.

p. 87: *On our first play date? You want to play Popo-kaki?* See note for p. 71.

p. 88: *Bad bag! I'm gonna break you open…and steal all your goodies!* See *Envy and Gratitude and Other Works.* Klein believed that an infant's aggression against the breast was partly rooted in the infant's envy of all the good things the breast seemed to contain.

p. 90: *Sculpture.* Bunnyman is not only a little Oedipus, but a little Leonardo too. And Leonardo once made a big horse sculpture for his favorite patron.

p. 91: *I'm afraid of horses.* See "Analysis of a Phobia in a Five-Year-Old Boy" (Little Hans, 1909). The name of my little black rabbit, Hans Klein, a.k.a. Little Hans, is obviously a nod to Freud's

Little Hans, who was afraid of horses. Melanie Klein apparently made the same nod when she named one of her sons Hans Klein.

p. 91: *Yup, Moses…Big Daddy!* Freud was a little obsessed with Moses and identified with him. He wrote the essay "The Moses of Michelangelo" in 1914 and a whole book on him toward the end of his life, *Moses and Monotheism*.

p. 93: *I can see your rage and your envy.* See *Envy and Gratitude and Other Works*. Klein was known for her work on rage and envy.

p. 93: *You're only right if I hate parts of you.* See *The Selected Melanie Klein*. Klein wrote about the nursing infant's aggression toward the mother's breast. She believed that "in the infant's mind the mother primarily appears as a good and bad breast split off from each other." (p. 53) The good breast is the one that appears whenever the baby wishes it to; the bad breast is the one that does not. That is, the bad breast, "the frustrating breast—attacked in oral-sadistic phantasies—is felt to be in fragments." But the good breast, "the gratifying breast, taken in under dominance of the sucking libido, is felt to be complete. This first internal good object acts as a focal point in the ego." (pp. 180–181)

p. 96: *It's my Squiggle Piggle!* See *The Piggle: An Account of the Psychoanalytic Treatment of a Little Girl*. The name Squiggle Piggle has a double derivation. One of Winnicott's analysands, who started therapy around age two, was nicknamed "The Piggle." And Winnicott invented the Squiggle Game. (See next note.)

p. 97: *Now you respond with your own squiggle…Respond?* See *Playing and Reality* by D.W. Winnicott (New York: Routledge, 1989), p. 16. In "Transitional Objects and Transitional Phenomena," the essay in which Winnicott described the infant's use of security blankets and teddy bears as transitional objects, he also described a simple drawing game he plays with his child patients: "In this squiggle game, I make some kind of an impulsive line-drawing and invite the child whom I am interviewing to turn it into something, and then he makes a squiggle for me to turn into something in my turn."

p. 99: *A yam…or a big empty ta-ta?* See *The Piggle*, pp. 52–53. Winnicott's patient the Piggle calls her mother's breasts "yams," sometimes even demanding, as her mother reports, "to suck my 'yams'." Also, the Piggle's imaginary "black mummy," who haunts her dreams, sometimes shouts out, "where are my yams, where are my yams?"

p. 99: *Mummy thinks everything's about her ta-tas.* Just as Freud came to be associated with penises and penis envy, so Klein came to be associated with breasts and breast envy, and not unjustly. Klein saw the mother's breast as the first thing that either satisfies or frustrates the child, and thus the first object toward which the child is envious or aggressive. See second note for p. 93.

p. 101: *Is it good or bad?* See *Object Relations in Psychoanalytic Theory*, p. 133. According to Klein, in very young children "all sensations are personified and attributed to good and bad objects." Klein noted: "in the very earliest stage every unpleasant stimulus is related to the 'bad,' denying, persecuting breasts, every pleasant stimulus to the 'good,' gratifying breasts." That is, the selfsame breast is perceived by the infant as the bad breast when it is not satisfying and as the good breast when it is.

p. 105: *empty speech bubble.* See *Écrits: A Selection* by Jacques Lacan, translated by Alan Sheridan. (London: Tavistock Publications, 1977) p. 45. According to Lacan, full speech, also called true speech, is when the speaker utters his real desires. But in empty speech, the subject is alienated from his wants. One of the tasks of the analyst is to figure out when full speech emerges from the analysand.

p. 105: *It's my Melanin Mum's black mammary!* See *The Piggle*, p. 44. Winnicott's patient known as "The Piggle," who began analysis when she was two years and four months old, was obsessed and tormented by an imaginary figure she called "the black mummy" and by the car that this black mummy drives, "the babacar." After two and a half years of intermittent therapy with Winnicott, from 1964 to 1966, in which the analyst took on the role of both the bad baby and the black mummy, the Piggle finally emerged, her mother reported (p. 200), as "unselfconscious—a spontaneous girl."

p. 107: *Oh no! I killed it!... Wait, I can do it again.* See *Playing and Reality*, pp. 92–94. In his essay "The Use of An Object," Winnicott described how a person can use an object (such as the mother's breast, or even a whole therapist) for his own purposes by attacking it and finding that it nonetheless survives. Winnicott noted, "This destruction becomes the unconscious backcloth for love of a real object...an object outside the area of the subject's omnipotent control."

p. 107: *Another squiggle...gone.* See *The Piggle*, p. 57. At one point in Winnicott's treatment of the Piggle, she plays with a deflated balloon.

p. 108: *Gone!* See *The Freud Reader*, edited by Peter Gay (New York: W.W. Norton & Company, 1989), p. 599. Years before Winnicott described what a child might get out of attacking an object and then watching it bounce back, Freud described a related joy: In *Beyond the Pleasure Principle*, Freud told of a little boy playing with a spool on a string: "What he did was to hold the reel by the string and very skillfully throw it over the edge of his curtained cot, so that it disappeared into it at the same time uttering his expressive 'o-o-o-o' [which meant *fort*, 'gone']. He then pulled the reel out of the cot again by the string and hailed its reappearance with a joyful '*da*' [there]." This is the game of *Fort-Da* (There-Gone or Disappearance and Return). By repeating it over and over the child has the illusion of controlling how and when things come and go. He has a feeling of omnipotence.

p. 109: *Be vewy vewy quiet.* Elmer Fudd's famous words, spoken in a stage whisper to his audience, are "Be vewy vewy quiet, I'm hunting wabbits!"

p. 110: *Wee-wee-wee-wee.* The Three Little Pigs say this when they run home.

p. 113: *I'm sure he's off sublimating somewhere.* See *The Freud Reader*, p. 454. Freud believed that Leonardo's passion for research (and perhaps for painting) was a form of sublimation, the redirection of libidinal energy into creative channels. He also noted a "concurrence in Leonardo of his over-powerful instinct for research and the atrophy of his sexual life..."

p. 116: *Did you know about that thing?* See *Delusion and Dream in Wilhelm Jensen's* Gradiva, by Sigmund Freud. (Los Angeles: Sun & Moon Classics, 1993). In this work, Freud analyzed the story of a man entranced by a Roman sculpture, a bas relief, of a Pompeiian woman walking.

p. 117: *What, in Michelangelo's name, is that?...It's Moses!*
Freud was fascinated by Moses and identified with him. See *The Freud-Jung Letters: The Correspondence Between Sigmund Freud and C.J. Jung* (Princeton: Princeton University Press, 1994), p. 93. In a 1904 letter to Carl Jung, Freud wrote: "If I am Moses, then you are Joshua and will take possession of the promised land of psychiatry, which I shall only be able to glimpse from afar." Winnicott shared Freud's fascination and identification with Moses. See *Winnicott: Life and Work*, by F. Robert Rodman, pp. 352–4.

p. 118: *Oh, c'mon, where's the wrath, man?* In "The Moses of Michelangelo" (*The Freud Reader*, p. 536), Freud tried to decipher exactly what moment in the Moses story Michelangelo had depicted in his sculpture. "What we see before us is not the inception of a violent action," Freud wrote, referring to the common interpretation that Moses is about to angrily break the tablets of the Ten Commandments. Rather, Freud wrote, Michelangelo's Moses "has overcome the temptation and he will now remain seated and still, in his frozen wrath and in his pain mingled with contempt." For the sake of the tablets, which "began to slide down and were in danger of being broken," Moses kept his emotions in check. While Freud noted the boldness in Michelangelo's decision to emend the Moses story to show a restrained Moses, Freud did *not* note the irony, and indeed the blasphemy, of Michelangelo's decision to turn Moses himself, the most famous enemy of idols and idol worshippers, into a statue, an idol!

p. 120: *I know you like Moses.* See *Freud: A Life for Our Time*, by Peter Gay, p. 317. Freud was clearly frustrated by his inability to control his followers, and this may have been part of the reason that he identified with Moses, who, one can argue, saw his own authority (in the form of the tablets) threatened by his childish followers (and their golden calf). In short, Freud's ideas about Moses, childhood omnipotence, and art seem to form a tight nexus. As Peter Gay notes in his Freud biography, Freud wrote to Sandor Ferenczi in 1912: "In my mood, I compare myself with the historical rather than with the Moses of Michelangelo I have interpreted."

p. 121: *Paranoid-schizoid...Depressive.* See *Introduction to the Work of Melanie Klein*, pp. 24–36. In the essays "A Contribution to the Psychogenesis of Manic Depressive States" (1934) and "Mourning in Relation to Manic Depressive States" (1940), Klein outlined two major states of relating to things in the world—the paranoid-schizoid position and the depressive position. For more on these, see second note for p. 69.

    p. 122: *I hate my Melanin mum.* One of the most striking things about Melanie Klein's daughter, Melitta, was her undisguised hatred of her mother. See notes for p. 68. Likewise, Melittle Klein finds her mother, Melanin, a dark dominatrix and persecutor.

    p. 123: *You'll feel like a god!* See *Playing and Reality*, p. 71. In his essay "Creativity and Its Origins," D.W. Winnicott noted that an infant's feeling of omnipotence was key to later well-being. The good-enough mother or the holding environment, he believed, would help to establish this omnipotent illusion, which would in turn help the child "cope with the immense shock of loss of omnipotence" later in life. The idea of the good-enough mother may be Winnicott's most lasting idea.

    p. 127: *You create...You destroy.* See *Totem and Taboo: Resemblances Between the Psychic Lives of Savages and Neurotics*, by Sigmund Freud, translated by Abraham Arden Brill (New York: Moffat, Yard & Company, 1918), pp. 148–149. In contrast to Winnicott, Freud believed that "omnipotence of thought," which he defined as "the unshaken confidence in [one's]...capacity to dominate the world," was a part of a primitive, neurotic belief system. Freud believed the only good modern outlet for omnipotence was art, in which "it still happens that man, consumed by his wishes, produces something similar to the gratification of these wishes....We rightly speak of the magic of art and compare the artist with a magician."

    p. 129: *Hey, could you guys cut me down?* See *Playing and Reality*, pp. 16–18. Rat Ma'am's use of the squiggle is similar to the way that one of Winnicott's young patients turned every squiggle into "something associated with a string...lasso, whip, crop, a yo-yo string, a string in a knot." One day the boy was found hanging upside down on a rope, playing dead. Winnicott suggested that the lasso-child "was dealing with a fear of separation, attempting to deny separation by his use of string..."

p. 130: *It will make you powerful...instead of cringing.* See *Playing and Reality*, p. 47. If a mother can play creatively with her baby, Winnicott said, then "the baby has some *experience* of magical control, that is, experience of that which is called 'omnipotence'..."

p. 131: *It's another line...Oooh, a line.* Every game of Squiggle begins with a line. (See note for p. 97.) The artist Saul Steinberg was fond of misquoting a famous line from Paul Klee. Klee said, "a line is a dot that went for a walk." Steinberg changed it to "a line is a thought that went for a walk." See *Saul Steinberg: A Biography*, by Deirdre Bair (New York: Nan A. Talese/Doubleday, 2012), p. 16.

p. 136: *Battle royale!!!* Thanks, Julius, for suggesting this scene!

p. 137: *Are we there yet? Are we there yet?* Think of Moses wandering in the desert with his skeptical followers...or think of Lisa and Bart Simpson on a car trip.

p. 141: *Shot...Thanatos...Eros...Thanatos.* See *Freud: A Life for Our Time*, pp. 401–402. "Thanatos" is what Freud called the death drive, "Eros" the love drive. They live in conflict. In 1919, after reading Schopenhauer, Freud decided that there are "two elemental pugnacious forces in the mind, Eros and Thanatos, locked in eternal battle."

p. 144: *Look! Me's on a beam!* Merriam-Webster's Dictionary translates the French *mise en abyme*, which literally means "placed into an abyss," as an image within an image or a story within a story. Thank you, Harry Cooper, for this pun.

p. 145: *And now we can eat our kill!* See *Freud: A Life for Our Time*, p. 644. Freud believed, Peter Gay notes, that the "Christian ceremony of Holy Communion" was a reenactment of the first totem meal.

p. 145: *After we eat our meal, we must banish the tools that did the deed.* Part of the purpose of the totem feast was for the celebrants to distance themselves from their original crime. See notes for p. 13.

p. 146: *Don't forget my pipe!* Hey, sometimes a pipe *is* just a pipe! The real Freud smoked a cigar.

p. 147: *Seeing his own Bunya-Boy take aim.* See *The Interpretation of Dreams* (1899), p. 296. Freud, who saw some of his battles with followers as Oedipal struggles, described Oedipus's plight with great sympathy: "His destiny moves us only because it might have been ours — because the Oracle laid the same curse upon us before our birth as upon him. It is the fate of all of us, perhaps, to direct our first sexual impulse towards our mother and our first hatred and our first murderous wish against our father. Our dreams convince us that this is so."

p. 150: *Mother May I?* If he manages to sit in the lap of his Moses Mummy, Bunnyman will achieve (in his way) the Oedipal goal of having his mother to himself. He will also demonstrate (in his way) the importance of what Winnicott called a good "holding environment." See *The Language of Winnicott*, pp. 193–198. Without a good holding environment, the infant's sense of being is "annihilated," Winnicott believed. His sense of self, his sense of "I AM," is threatened. An infant must be held. "The infant...only understands love that is expressed in physical terms, that is to say, by live, human holding." This is also true for Bunnyman.

ACKNOWLEDGMENTS

Most of all, I would like to thank my extraordinary husband, Harry Cooper, special effects man, upbeat editor, and (still) in-house optimist. My sister, Susan Boxer, a psychologist with a poet's ear, introduced me to the world of object relations. My father, Phillip Boxer, passed on his love of Freud. My mother, Florine Boxer, is the sharpest of readers. My uncle Bill Thorn was the first fan of my comics. I am grateful to Arnie Richards and Tamar and Larry Schwartz of IP Books for taking me on board their psychoanalytic ship. I feel lucky to have had the amazing designer Margaret Bauer along for the ride. I would also like to acknowledge Len Rizzi, who took great care in photographing my drawings. I will always be indebted to the people who have shown, in various ways, their belief in me and my post-Floydian project: Alison Bechdel, Andrew Blauner, Sarah Funke Butler, Joan Harvey, Jeet Heer, Drew Joseph, Austin Ratner, and Peter Stein. A special thanks goes to my most trenchantly cutting editor, Michael Frank. And I give a big hug to my son the empath, Julius Boxer-Cooper, who helped me with the drawings of weaponry.

ABOUT THE AUTHOR

Sarah Boxer is the creator of the cartoon novel *In the Floyd Archives* and the editor of *Ultimate Blogs: Masterworks from the Wild Web*. She is a contributing writer at *The Atlantic* and a critic who writes for *The New York Review of Books*, *The L.A. Review of Books*, *The New York Times Book Review*, *The Comics Journal*, *Artforum*, and *Photograph*. For many years she was on the staff of *The New York Times*, where she was an editor, critic, and reporter covering animals, art, language, philosophy, photography, and psychoanalysis. Born in Denver, she lives with her husband and son in Washington, D.C. There she is working on a series of Shakespearean tragic-comics, including *Hamlet: Prince of Pigs*.

photo: Jo Anne Schlesinger